Haikus (

366 Haiku Starters

Laurel McHargue

ALPHA PEAK LLC   Leadville, CO

Haikus Can Amuse!
366 Haiku Starters

Published by Alpha Peak LLC
Leadville, CO

McHargue, Laurel, Author
Haikus Can Amuse! 366 Haiku Starters

ISBN: 978-0-9969711-5-7

Cover Design by Kostis Pavlou
Back Cover Photo by *Tonya's Captured Inspirations LLC*

PRINTED IN THE UNITED STATES OF AMERICA

Haikus Can Amuse!

366 Haiku Starters

Dedicated to
the poet hidden in you
Let your poet out!

Haikus* Can Amuse!
366 Haiku Starters

* The plural of haiku is simply haiku.
I used my poetic license** with the title.

(** *not* available at your local DMV)

A most basic understanding of the Japanese poetic haiku form is all you'll need to enjoy your haiku starter journal. Throughout my years of teaching haiku to students of all ages, I've enjoyed watching the intensity of effort required to express often silly—and more often profound—thought in seventeen succinct syllables. Inevitably, fingers fidget or tap softly on desktops and leg tops as initially reluctant boys and girls count out syllables, smiling when they solve their puzzle. Even those who "hate English" find fulfillment in fitting words into the satisfying symmetry of syllables spread across three lines: first 5, then 7, then 5, for a total of 17 syllables to complete a poem.

I'd award 17 points for 17 strong syllables and warn students they'd receive no points for lame ones like "a" or "the" or "like" or "and" or repeated words, but I'm not your teacher. Many of my haiku starters have lame syllables. And remember, your work in this journal is designed to encourage a habit of **stress-free** creativity. No one is grading you. Open your mind and let your ideas flow. This is for you.

There are pages for 366 days (because every year should have an extra day!) numbered simply 1-366 with space for you to fill in your own day and date (because you don't need the stress of a daily requirement). Use the first line of 5 syllables to inspire a thought or memory, and then complete the haiku on the next two lines with 7 syllables on the middle line and 5 syllables on the last line. There's no need to consider rhyme at all.

In some cases, your haiku starter is just one five-syllable word, so don't let that throw you. As with other multi-word starters, think about the word and what it might mean to you. Don't worry about punctuation either; there are no strict rules on capitalization or punctuation for haiku. Each line does not need to be a complete sentence; your whole poem might be a single seventeen-syllable sentence. And your last line may come as a surprise to you. If it does, you've captured a more complex essence of haiku!

Some of the starters are quite silly, but some may take you to poignant places. Even if you have no experience with the haiku starter—for example, you may never have experienced a "Creaky attic floor" or "Messy morning hair"—try to imagine the experience anyway or pretend it refers to someone else. Also, feel free to substitute for words like "I/me" with "she/her," "he/him," "they/them/we/you" . . . you get the idea . . . if it helps.

On every 10th page you'll find a vague TOPIC suggestion instead of a completed first line. These pages are designed to give you complete creative freedom for the full 17 syllables.

Once you've completed your haiku—use pen or pencil or crayon!—spend just a few minutes jotting down (in narrative form, as you would in a journal) what inspired your haiku. Allow yourself to laugh or cry or wonder. Haiku can provoke powerful emotions. Go ahead and doodle in the margins if you'd like! This is *your* workbook.

At the end of the book you'll find complete examples of haiku written by guest contributors. If the 366 pages in this journal just aren't enough for you, feel free to use some of their first lines—or last lines—to start your own unique poem.

When you get to #366, whenever you get to it, you'll have completed a Leap Year's worth of poems and contemplations! Who knows? Perhaps you'll publish your compilation someday.

* * * *I must now present this warning:* * * *

Don't be surprised when you discover yourself thinking in haiku at random times each day as you become more comfortable with focusing your attention on short bursts of expression. Just be ready to answer the question, "So, what is it you're counting?" when you're caught tapping out 5 . . . 7 . . . 5!

But enough of this preamble. Jump in, have fun, work through the pages as quickly or slowly as you wish, and DON'T STRESS!

Haikus can amuse   [5 syllables]

Discipline your chatterbox   [7 syllables]

Express succinctly   [5 syllables]

Haiku trains your brain   [5 syllables]

for seventeen syllables   [7 syllables]

captured brilliantly   [5 syllables]

And now it's your turn   [5 syllables]

Impress yourself and have fun   [7 syllables]

counting on fingers   [5 syllables]

Got it? [2 syllables]

1: _____

Outside my window

_____

_____

My thoughts . . .

_____

_____

_____

_____

_____

_____

_____

_____

2: _____

Phone falls in ocean

_____

_____

My thoughts . . .

_____

_____

_____

_____

_____

_____

_____

_____

3: _____

Learning never ends

_____

_____

My thoughts . . .

_____

_____

_____

_____

_____

_____

_____

_____

4: _____

Friends always tell me

_____

_____

My thoughts . . .

_____

_____

_____

_____

_____

_____

_____

_____

_____

5: _____

One perfect moment

_____

_____

My thoughts . . .

_____

_____

_____

_____

_____

_____

_____

_____

6: _____

Counting on fingers

_____

_____

My thoughts . . .

_____

_____

_____

_____

_____

_____

_____

_____

7: _____

Monster appetite

_____

_____

My thoughts . . .

_____

_____

_____

_____

_____

_____

_____

_____

8: _____

Thinking of parents

_____

_____

My thoughts . . .

_____

_____

_____

_____

_____

_____

_____

_____

9: _____

So many choices

_____

_____

My thoughts . . .

_____

_____

_____

_____

_____

_____

_____

_____

_____

* 10: _____

_____

_____

_____

* Topic: JOY

My thoughts . . .

_____

_____

_____

_____

_____

_____

_____

_____

_____

11: _____

Thoughts are like magpies

_____

_____

My thoughts . . .

_____

_____

_____

_____

_____

_____

_____

_____

12: _____

Loved one lies dying

_____

_____

My thoughts ...

_____

_____

_____

_____

_____

_____

_____

_____

_____

13: _____

Nebulous success

_____

_____

My thoughts . . .

_____

_____

_____

_____

_____

_____

_____

_____

_____

14: _____

Today my heart says

_____

_____

My thoughts . . .

_____

_____

_____

_____

_____

_____

_____

_____

15: _____

What I would whisper

_____

_____

My thoughts . . .

_____

_____

_____

_____

_____

_____

_____

16: _____

What you learn today

_____

_____

My thoughts . . .

_____

_____

_____

_____

_____

_____

_____

_____

17: _____

Earthworm on the street

_____

_____

My thoughts . . .

_____

_____

_____

_____

_____

_____

_____

_____

_____

18: _____

My superpower

_____

_____

My thoughts . . .

_____

_____

_____

_____

_____

_____

_____

_____

19: _____

All I really know

_____

_____

My thoughts . . .

_____

_____

_____

_____

_____

_____

_____

_____

* 20: _____

_____

_____

_____

* Topic: Summer

My thoughts . . .

_____

_____

_____

_____

_____

_____

_____

_____

21: _____

April showers bring

_____

_____

My thoughts . . .

_____

_____

_____

_____

_____

_____

_____

_____

_____

22: _____

When in doubt, always

_____

_____

My thoughts . . .

_____

_____

_____

_____

_____

_____

_____

_____

23: _____

Animal people

_____

_____

My thoughts . . .

_____

_____

_____

_____

_____

_____

_____

_____

24: _____

Never say "sorry"

_____

_____

My thoughts . . .

_____

_____

_____

_____

_____

_____

_____

_____

25: _____

Children singing songs

_____

_____

My thoughts . . .

_____

_____

_____

_____

_____

_____

_____

_____

_____

26: _____

Hamburgers, hot dogs

_____

_____

My thoughts . . .

_____

_____

_____

_____

_____

_____

_____

_____

_____

27: _____

Waiting for something

_____

_____

My thoughts . . .

_____

_____

_____

_____

_____

_____

_____

_____

28: _____

Crunchy autumn leaves

_____

_____

My thoughts . . .

_____

_____

_____

_____

_____

_____

_____

_____

29: _____

Anger never can

_____

_____

My thoughts . . .

_____

_____

_____

_____

_____

_____

_____

_____

_____

* 30: _____

_____

_____

_____

* Topic: Heat

My thoughts . . .

_____

_____

_____

_____

_____

_____

_____

_____

31: _____

Strangers don't know me

_____

_____

My thoughts . . .

_____

_____

_____

_____

_____

_____

_____

_____

_____

32: _____

Fog-enshrouded hills

_____

_____

My thoughts . . .

_____

_____

_____

_____

_____

_____

_____

_____

33: _____

Memories of pain

_____

_____

My thoughts . . .

_____

_____

_____

_____

_____

_____

_____

_____

_____

34: _____

Silly childhood dreams

_____

_____

My thoughts . . .

_____

_____

_____

_____

_____

_____

_____

_____

_____

35: _____

Best teachers always

_____

_____

My thoughts . . .

_____

_____

_____

_____

_____

_____

_____

_____

_____

_____

36: _____

Crazy creation

_____

_____

My thoughts . . .

_____

_____

_____

_____

_____

_____

_____

_____

37: _____

Vanilla ice cream

_____

_____

My thoughts . . .

_____

_____

_____

_____

_____

_____

_____

_____

_____

38: _____

Forgotten birthday

_____

_____

My thoughts . . .

_____

_____

_____

_____

_____

_____

_____

_____

39: _____

When I was seven

_____

_____

My thoughts . . .

_____

_____

_____

_____

_____

_____

_____

_____

* 40: _____

_____

_____

_____

* Topic: Togetherness

My thoughts . . .

_____

_____

_____

_____

_____

_____

_____

_____

41: _____

Old-timers must know

_____

_____

My thoughts ...

_____

_____

_____

_____

_____

_____

_____

_____

_____

42: _____

How could anyone

_____

_____

My thoughts . . .

_____

_____

_____

_____

_____

_____

_____

_____

43: _____

My first injury

_____

_____

My thoughts . . .

_____

_____

_____

_____

_____

_____

_____

_____

44: _____

Teenage years filled with

_____

_____

My thoughts . . .

_____

_____

_____

_____

_____

_____

_____

_____

_____

45: _____

What humans possess

_____

_____

My thoughts . . .

_____

_____

_____

_____

_____

_____

_____

_____

_____

46: _____

Crystal teardrops fall

_____

_____

My thoughts . . .

_____

_____

_____

_____

_____

_____

_____

_____

47: _____

Overburdened brain

_____

_____

My thoughts . . .

_____

_____

_____

_____

_____

_____

_____

_____

48: _____

Stampeding horses

_____

_____

My thoughts . . .

_____

_____

_____

_____

_____

_____

_____

_____

49: _____

Stinky old gym clothes

_____

_____

My thoughts . . .

_____

_____

_____

_____

_____

_____

_____

_____

_____

* 50: _____

_____

_____

_____

* Topic: Fear

My thoughts . . .

_____

_____

_____

_____

_____

_____

_____

_____

_____

51: _____

Asking forgiveness

_____

_____

My thoughts . . .

_____

_____

_____

_____

_____

_____

_____

_____

_____

52: _____

Secret indulgence

_____

_____

My thoughts . . .

_____

_____

_____

_____

_____

_____

_____

_____

_____

53: _____

Bright winter sunrise

_____

_____

My thoughts . . .

_____

_____

_____

_____

_____

_____

_____

_____

54: _____

When I hear your name

_____

_____

My thoughts . . .

_____

_____

_____

_____

_____

_____

_____

_____

55: _____

Should I grow quite old

_____

_____

My thoughts . . .

_____

_____

_____

_____

_____

_____

_____

_____

56: _____

Listen closely now

_____

_____

My thoughts . . .

_____

_____

_____

_____

_____

_____

_____

_____

57: _____

Social media

_____

_____

My thoughts . . .

_____

_____

_____

_____

_____

_____

_____

_____

_____

58: _____

Who really knows why

_____

_____

My thoughts . . .

_____

_____

_____

_____

_____

_____

_____

_____

_____

59: _____

Heat mirage ripples

_____

_____

My thoughts . . .

_____

_____

_____

_____

_____

_____

_____

_____

_____

* 60: _____

_____

_____

_____

* Topic: Green

My thoughts . . .

_____

_____

_____

_____

_____

_____

_____

_____

_____

_____

61: _____

Brothers and sisters

_____

_____

My thoughts . . .

_____

_____

_____

_____

_____

_____

_____

_____

_____

62: _____

Woodpecker drumming

_____

_____

My thoughts . . .

_____

_____

_____

_____

_____

_____

_____

_____

63: _____

Wondering why I

_____

_____

My thoughts . . .

_____

_____

_____

_____

_____

_____

_____

_____

64: _____

One, three, five, seven

_____

_____

My thoughts . . .

_____

_____

_____

_____

_____

_____

_____

_____

65: _____

Eyes can only see

_____

_____

My thoughts . . .

_____

_____

_____

_____

_____

_____

_____

_____

_____

66: _____

Never forever

_____

_____

My thoughts . . .

_____

_____

_____

_____

_____

_____

_____

_____

_____

67: _____

Wild animals roam

_____

_____

My thoughts . . .

_____

_____

_____

_____

_____

_____

_____

_____

_____

68: _____

Serendipity

_____

_____

My thoughts . . .

_____

_____

_____

_____

_____

_____

_____

_____

_____

69: _____

Sand between my toes

_____

_____

My thoughts . . .

_____

_____

_____

_____

_____

_____

_____

_____

_____

* 70: _____

_____

_____

_____

* Topic: Children

My thoughts . . .

_____

_____

_____

_____

_____

_____

_____

_____

_____

71: _____

Stray dog whimpering

_____

_____

My thoughts . . .

_____

_____

_____

_____

_____

_____

_____

_____

_____

72: _____

Soft snowflakes falling

_____

_____

My thoughts . . .

_____

_____

_____

_____

_____

_____

_____

_____

_____

73: _____

Incessant chatter

_____

_____

My thoughts . . .

_____

_____

_____

_____

_____

_____

_____

_____

74: _____

Unexpected news

_____

_____

My thoughts . . .

_____

_____

_____

_____

_____

_____

_____

_____

_____

75: _____

Frisky new kitten

_____

_____

My thoughts . . .

_____

_____

_____

_____

_____

_____

_____

_____

76: _____

Crisp, juicy apple

_____

_____

My thoughts . . .

_____

_____

_____

_____

_____

_____

_____

_____

77: _____

I'm not like others

_____

_____

My thoughts . . .

_____

_____

_____

_____

_____

_____

_____

_____

78: _____

The end of the world

_____

_____

My thoughts . . .

_____

_____

_____

_____

_____

_____

_____

_____

79: _____

Sunshine makes me squint

_____

_____

My thoughts . . .

_____

_____

_____

_____

_____

_____

_____

_____

_____

* 80: _____

_____

_____

_____

* Topic: Water

My thoughts . . .

_____

_____

_____

_____

_____

_____

_____

_____

_____

81: _____

Frost covered tulips

_____

_____

My thoughts . . .

_____

_____

_____

_____

_____

_____

_____

_____

_____

82: _____

Silly syllables

_____

_____

My thoughts . . .

_____

_____

_____

_____

_____

_____

_____

_____

_____

83: _____

Tossing in my sleep

_____

_____

My thoughts . . .

_____

_____

_____

_____

_____

_____

_____

_____

_____

84: _____

Bluebird looks at me

_____

_____

My thoughts . . .

_____

_____

_____

_____

_____

_____

_____

_____

_____

85: _____

Stormy ocean heaves

_____

_____

My thoughts . . .

_____

_____

_____

_____

_____

_____

_____

_____

_____

86: _____

Risk, reward, choices

_____

_____

My thoughts . . .

_____

_____

_____

_____

_____

_____

_____

_____

87: _____

Yellow bus waiting

_____

_____

My thoughts . . .

_____

_____

_____

_____

_____

_____

_____

_____

88: _____

Messy morning hair

_____

_____

My thoughts . . .

_____

_____

_____

_____

_____

_____

_____

_____

89: _____

Breathing heavily

_____

_____

My thoughts . . .

_____

_____

_____

_____

_____

_____

_____

_____

_____

* 90: _____

_____

_____

_____

* Topic: Courage

My thoughts . . .

_____

_____

_____

_____

_____

_____

_____

_____

91: _____

Special birthday gift

_____

_____

My thoughts . . .

_____

_____

_____

_____

_____

_____

_____

_____

_____

92: _____

Homeless woman sits

_____

_____

My thoughts . . .

_____

_____

_____

_____

_____

_____

_____

_____

93: _____

Personality

_____

_____

My thoughts . . .

_____

_____

_____

_____

_____

_____

_____

_____

_____

94: _____

If only I'd known

_____

_____

My thoughts . . .

_____

_____

_____

_____

_____

_____

_____

_____

_____

95: _____

Must be mistaken

_____

_____

My thoughts . . .

_____

_____

_____

_____

_____

_____

_____

_____

_____

96: _____

Spirits soaring high

_____

_____

My thoughts . . .

_____

_____

_____

_____

_____

_____

_____

_____

97: _____

Smudge on my window

_____

_____

My thoughts . . .

_____

_____

_____

_____

_____

_____

_____

_____

98: _____

Push against limits

_____

_____

My thoughts . . .

_____

_____

_____

_____

_____

_____

_____

_____

99: _____

Ev'ryday wishes

_____

_____

My thoughts . . .

_____

_____

_____

_____

_____

_____

_____

_____

_____

* 100: _____

_____

_____

_____

* Topic: Red

My thoughts . . .

_____

_____

_____

_____

_____

_____

_____

101: _____

Post-Thanksgiving nap

_____

_____

My thoughts ...

_____

_____

_____

_____

_____

_____

_____

_____

102: _____

Spinach makes you strong

_____

_____

My thoughts . . .

_____

_____

_____

_____

_____

_____

_____

_____

103: _____

Keeping my mouth shut

_____

_____

My thoughts . . .

_____

_____

_____

_____

_____

_____

_____

_____

104: _____

Transfiguration

_____

_____

My thoughts . . .

_____

_____

_____

_____

_____

_____

_____

_____

_____

105: _____

Lightning-shattered tree

_____

_____

My thoughts . . .

_____

_____

_____

_____

_____

_____

_____

_____

_____

106: _____

Shared secret glances

_____

_____

My thoughts . . .

_____

_____

_____

_____

_____

_____

_____

_____

107: _____

Feeling like screaming

_____

_____

My thoughts . . .

_____

_____

_____

_____

_____

_____

_____

_____

108: _____

Fasten seatbelts, please

_____

_____

My thoughts . . .

_____

_____

_____

_____

_____

_____

_____

_____

_____

109: _____

Neighbors can be kind

_____

_____

My thoughts . . .

_____

_____

_____

_____

_____

_____

_____

_____

* 110: _____

_____

_____

_____

* Topic: Autumn

My thoughts . . .

_____

_____

_____

_____

_____

_____

_____

_____

111: _____

Chicken, beef, or fish

_____

_____

My thoughts . . .

_____

_____

_____

_____

_____

_____

_____

_____

112: _____

Swirling bubbles float

_____

_____

My thoughts . . .

_____

_____

_____

_____

_____

_____

_____

_____

113: _____

Pristine mountain lake

_____

_____

My thoughts . . .

_____

_____

_____

_____

_____

_____

_____

_____

114: _____

Unrelenting fear

_____

_____

My thoughts . . .

_____

_____

_____

_____

_____

_____

_____

_____

115: _____

Countless twinkling stars

_____

_____

My thoughts . . .

_____

_____

_____

_____

_____

_____

_____

_____

_____

116: _____

Caged old lion roars

_____

_____

My thoughts . . .

_____

_____

_____

_____

_____

_____

_____

_____

_____

117: _____

Just before thunder

_____

_____

My thoughts . . .

_____

_____

_____

_____

_____

_____

_____

_____

118: _____

Light flickers within

_____

_____

My thoughts . . .

_____

_____

_____

_____

_____

_____

_____

_____

_____

119: _____

Icy river melts

_____

_____

My thoughts . . .

_____

_____

_____

_____

_____

_____

_____

_____

* 120: _____

_____

_____

_____

* Topic: Storm

My thoughts . . .

_____

_____

_____

_____

_____

_____

_____

_____

_____

121: _____

Creaky attic floor

_____

_____

My thoughts . . .

_____

_____

_____

_____

_____

_____

_____

_____

122: _____

Ancient ruins wait

_____

_____

My thoughts . . .

_____

_____

_____

_____

_____

_____

_____

_____

123: _____

Hearing my name called

_____

_____

My thoughts . . .

_____

_____

_____

_____

_____

_____

_____

_____

124: _____

Water ev'rywhere

_____

_____

My thoughts . . .

_____

_____

_____

_____

_____

_____

_____

_____

125: _____

Ubiquitous hope

_____

_____

My thoughts . . .

_____

_____

_____

_____

_____

_____

_____

_____

126: _____

Trying not to laugh

_____

_____

My thoughts . . .

_____

_____

_____

_____

_____

_____

_____

_____

127: _____

Dripping ice cream cone

_____

_____

My thoughts . . .

_____

_____

_____

_____

_____

_____

_____

_____

128: _____

Mirror reflects truth

_____

_____

My thoughts . . .

_____

_____

_____

_____

_____

_____

_____

_____

_____

129: _____

Ten toes, ten fingers

_____

_____

My thoughts . . .

_____

_____

_____

_____

_____

_____

_____

_____

* 130: _____

_____

_____

_____

* Topic: Pride

My thoughts . . .

_____

_____

_____

_____

_____

_____

_____

_____

131: _____

Crackling flames rise high

_____

_____

My thoughts . . .

_____

_____

_____

_____

_____

_____

_____

_____

132: _____

Polka dot clothing

_____

_____

My thoughts . . .

_____

_____

_____

_____

_____

_____

_____

_____

_____

133: _____

Exciting future

_____

_____

My thoughts . . .

_____

_____

_____

_____

_____

_____

_____

_____

134: _____

Blades of grass push through

_____

_____

My thoughts . . .

_____

_____

_____

_____

_____

_____

_____

_____

135: _____

Never-ending dream

_____

_____

My thoughts . . .

_____

_____

_____

_____

_____

_____

_____

_____

136: _____

Choking on my words

_____

_____

My thoughts . . .

_____

_____

_____

_____

_____

_____

_____

_____

137: _____

Mist lifts from water

_____

_____

My thoughts . . .

_____

_____

_____

_____

_____

_____

_____

_____

138: _____

Satisfying crunch

_____

_____

My thoughts . . .

_____

_____

_____

_____

_____

_____

_____

_____

_____

139: _____

Disregarding time

_____

_____

My thoughts . . .

_____

_____

_____

_____

_____

_____

_____

_____

* 140: _____

_____

_____

_____

* Topic: Blue

My thoughts . . .

_____

_____

_____

_____

_____

_____

_____

_____

_____

141: _____

Abundant garden

_____

_____

My thoughts . . .

_____

_____

_____

_____

_____

_____

_____

_____

142: _____

Goosebumps on my arms

_____

_____

My thoughts . . .

_____

_____

_____

_____

_____

_____

_____

_____

143: _____

Wild horses gallop

_____

_____

My thoughts . . .

_____

_____

_____

_____

_____

_____

_____

_____

144: _____

Sheet of ice shatters

_____

_____

My thoughts . . .

_____

_____

_____

_____

_____

_____

_____

_____

_____

145: _____

Car speeds recklessly

_____

_____

My thoughts . . .

_____

_____

_____

_____

_____

_____

_____

_____

146: _____

Something in my eye

_____

_____

My thoughts . . .

_____

_____

_____

_____

_____

_____

_____

_____

147: _____

Hot-chicken-soup days

_____

_____

My thoughts . . .

_____

_____

_____

_____

_____

_____

_____

_____

148: _____

Grandpa drank whiskey

_____

_____

My thoughts . . .

_____

_____

_____

_____

_____

_____

_____

_____

_____

149: _____

Evolving Earth spins

_____

_____

My thoughts . . .

_____

_____

_____

_____

_____

_____

_____

_____

* 150: _____

_____

_____

_____

* Topic: Confusion

My thoughts . . .

_____

_____

_____

_____

_____

_____

_____

_____

_____

151: _____

Molten lava creeps

_____

_____

My thoughts . . .

_____

_____

_____

_____

_____

_____

_____

_____

152: _____

Frantic bumblebees

_____

_____

My thoughts . . .

_____

_____

_____

_____

_____

_____

_____

_____

153: _____

Golf-ball-size hail storm

_____

_____

My thoughts . . .

_____

_____

_____

_____

_____

_____

_____

_____

154: _____

Breaking from my past

_____

_____

My thoughts . . .

_____

_____

_____

_____

_____

_____

_____

_____

155: _____

Red Jell-O jiggles

_____

_____

My thoughts . . .

_____

_____

_____

_____

_____

_____

_____

_____

156: _____

Searching for answers

_____

_____

My thoughts . . .

_____

_____

_____

_____

_____

_____

_____

_____

157: _____

Dance like a goofball

_____

_____

My thoughts . . .

_____

_____

_____

_____

_____

_____

_____

_____

158: _____

Don't step on the cracks

_____

_____

My thoughts . . .

_____

_____

_____

_____

_____

_____

_____

_____

159: _____

Monday morning comes

_____

_____

My thoughts . . .

_____

_____

_____

_____

_____

_____

_____

_____

* 160: _____

_____

_____

_____

* Topic: Mountains

My thoughts . . .

_____

_____

_____

_____

_____

_____

_____

_____

161: _____

Paper or plastic

_____

_____

My thoughts . . .

_____

_____

_____

_____

_____

_____

_____

_____

162: _____

Desert dust devils

_____

_____

My thoughts . . .

_____

_____

_____

_____

_____

_____

_____

_____

_____

163: _____

Soldiers risk their lives

_____

_____

My thoughts . . .

_____

_____

_____

_____

_____

_____

_____

_____

164: _____

New box of crayons

_____

_____

My thoughts . . .

_____

_____

_____

_____

_____

_____

_____

_____

165: _____

Salty ocean air

_____

_____

My thoughts . . .

_____

_____

_____

_____

_____

_____

_____

_____

_____

166: _____

Icarus had dreams

_____

_____

My thoughts . . .

_____

_____

_____

_____

_____

_____

_____

_____

167: _____

Flesh, bones, blood, brain, soul

_____

_____

My thoughts . . .

_____

_____

_____

_____

_____

_____

_____

_____

168: _____

Deep ocean currents

_____

_____

My thoughts . . .

_____

_____

_____

_____

_____

_____

_____

_____

169: _____

Hieroglyphics speak

_____

_____

My thoughts . . .

_____

_____

_____

_____

_____

_____

_____

_____

_____

* 170: _____

_____

_____

_____

* Topic: Trust

My thoughts . . .

_____

_____

_____

_____

_____

_____

_____

_____

171: _____

Love lasts forever

_____

_____

My thoughts . . .

_____

_____

_____

_____

_____

_____

_____

_____

172: _____

Graduation day

_____

_____

My thoughts . . .

_____

_____

_____

_____

_____

_____

_____

_____

_____

173: _____

Waking in darkness

_____

_____

My thoughts . . .

_____

_____

_____

_____

_____

_____

_____

_____

174: _____

Innocent children

_____

_____

My thoughts . . .

_____

_____

_____

_____

_____

_____

_____

_____

175: _____

Hackles raised on dog

_____

_____

My thoughts . . .

_____

_____

_____

_____

_____

_____

_____

_____

176: _____

Wedding day jitters

_____

_____

My thoughts . . .

_____

_____

_____

_____

_____

_____

_____

_____

_____

177: _____

Though you may not know

_____

_____

My thoughts . . .

_____

_____

_____

_____

_____

_____

_____

_____

178: _____

Candle flame flickers

_____

_____

My thoughts . . .

_____

_____

_____

_____

_____

_____

_____

_____

179: _____

Walking on eggshells

_____

_____

My thoughts . . .

_____

_____

_____

_____

_____

_____

_____

_____

* 180: _____

_____

_____

_____

* Topic: Black

My thoughts . . .

_____

_____

_____

_____

_____

_____

_____

_____

_____

181: _____

Firstborn privilege

_____

_____

My thoughts . . .

_____

_____

_____

_____

_____

_____

_____

_____

182: _____

Falling off my bike

_____

_____

My thoughts . . .

_____

_____

_____

_____

_____

_____

_____

_____

183: _____

Blistering sunburn

_____

_____

My thoughts . . .

_____

_____

_____

_____

_____

_____

_____

_____

184: _____

Slurping spaghetti

_____

_____

My thoughts . . .

_____

_____

_____

_____

_____

_____

_____

_____

185: _____

l, m, n, o, p

_____

_____

My thoughts . . .

_____

_____

_____

_____

_____

_____

_____

_____

186: _____

Fresh wild blueberries

_____

_____

My thoughts . . .

_____

_____

_____

_____

_____

_____

_____

_____

187: _____

Clouds blot out the sun

_____

_____

My thoughts . . .

_____

_____

_____

_____

_____

_____

_____

_____

188: _____

Butterfly daydreams

_____

_____

My thoughts . . .

_____

_____

_____

_____

_____

_____

_____

_____

189: _____

Get around to it

_____

_____

My thoughts . . .

_____

_____

_____

_____

_____

_____

_____

_____

* 190: _____

_____

_____

_____

* Topic: Adolescence

My thoughts . . .

_____

_____

_____

_____

_____

_____

_____

_____

_____

191: _____

Little white lies grow

_____

_____

My thoughts . . .

_____

_____

_____

_____

_____

_____

_____

_____

_____

192: _____

Technology wins

_____

_____

My thoughts . . .

_____

_____

_____

_____

_____

_____

_____

_____

193: _____

Biting fingernails

_____

_____

My thoughts . . .

_____

_____

_____

_____

_____

_____

_____

_____

194: _____

Showing up naked

_____

_____

My thoughts . . .

_____

_____

_____

_____

_____

_____

_____

_____

_____

195: _____

What's it all about

_____

_____

My thoughts . . .

_____

_____

_____

_____

_____

_____

_____

_____

_____

196: _____

Ninety-nine bottles

_____

_____

My thoughts . . .

_____

_____

_____

_____

_____

_____

_____

_____

_____

197: _____

Ignoring the signs

_____

_____

My thoughts . . .

_____

_____

_____

_____

_____

_____

_____

_____

_____

198: _____

Squirrel hides his nuts

_____

_____

My thoughts . . .

_____

_____

_____

_____

_____

_____

_____

_____

_____

199: _____

So much more to do

_____

_____

My thoughts . . .

_____

_____

_____

_____

_____

_____

_____

_____

_____

* 200: _____

_____

_____

_____

* Topic: Winter

My thoughts . . .

_____

_____

_____

_____

_____

_____

_____

_____

201: _____

I can handle truth

_____

_____

My thoughts . . .

_____

_____

_____

_____

_____

_____

_____

_____

_____

202: _____

Snuggling in blankets

_____

_____

My thoughts . . .

_____

_____

_____

_____

_____

_____

_____

_____

203: _____

Last day of summer

_____

_____

My thoughts . . .

_____

_____

_____

_____

_____

_____

_____

_____

_____

204: _____

Monkeys are funny

_____

_____

My thoughts . . .

_____

_____

_____

_____

_____

_____

_____

_____

_____

205: _____

Eyes make first contact

_____

_____

My thoughts . . .

_____

_____

_____

_____

_____

_____

_____

_____

_____

206: _____

Biting hot pizza

_____

_____

My thoughts . . .

_____

_____

_____

_____

_____

_____

_____

_____

207: _____

Living on my own

_____

_____

My thoughts . . .

_____

_____

_____

_____

_____

_____

_____

_____

208: _____

Mossy forest floor

_____

_____

My thoughts . . .

_____

_____

_____

_____

_____

_____

_____

_____

_____

209: _____

Fingernails, blackboards

_____

_____

My thoughts . . .

_____

_____

_____

_____

_____

_____

_____

_____

_____

* 210: _____

_____

_____

_____

* Topic: Anger

My thoughts . . .

_____

_____

_____

_____

_____

_____

_____

_____

_____

211: _____

Sultry summer night

_____

_____

My thoughts . . .

_____

_____

_____

_____

_____

_____

_____

_____

_____

212: _____

Water up my nose

_____

_____

My thoughts . . .

_____

_____

_____

_____

_____

_____

_____

_____

_____

213: _____

Heavy eyelids droop

_____

_____

My thoughts . . .

_____

_____

_____

_____

_____

_____

_____

_____

_____

214: _____

Building sand castles

_____

_____

My thoughts . . .

_____

_____

_____

_____

_____

_____

_____

_____

_____

215: _____

Slobbery dog kiss

_____

_____

My thoughts . . .

_____

_____

_____

_____

_____

_____

_____

_____

216: _____

Visiting in-laws

_____

_____

My thoughts . . .

_____

_____

_____

_____

_____

_____

_____

_____

_____

217: _____

Hairs freeze in my nose

_____

_____

My thoughts . . .

_____

_____

_____

_____

_____

_____

_____

_____

_____

218: _____

Firecrackers explode

_____

_____

My thoughts . . .

_____

_____

_____

_____

_____

_____

_____

_____

219: _____

There once was a man

_____

_____

My thoughts . . .

_____

_____

_____

_____

_____

_____

_____

_____

_____

* 220: _____

_____

_____

_____

* Topic: Determination

My thoughts . . .

_____

_____

_____

_____

_____

_____

_____

_____

_____

221: _____

Food stuck in my teeth

_____

_____

My thoughts . . .

_____

_____

_____

_____

_____

_____

_____

_____

222: _____

Black, billowing smoke

_____

_____

My thoughts . . .

_____

_____

_____

_____

_____

_____

_____

_____

223: _____

Wading through worries

_____

_____

My thoughts . . .

_____

_____

_____

_____

_____

_____

_____

_____

_____

224: _____

First winter snowfall

_____

_____

My thoughts . . .

_____

_____

_____

_____

_____

_____

_____

_____

225: _____

Full moon just rising

_____

_____

My thoughts . . .

_____

_____

_____

_____

_____

_____

_____

_____

_____

226: _____

Wrinkles on my face

_____

_____

My thoughts . . .

_____

_____

_____

_____

_____

_____

_____

_____

_____

_____

227: _____

Say please and thank you

_____

_____

My thoughts . . .

_____

_____

_____

_____

_____

_____

_____

_____

_____

228: _____

Wishing on a star

_____

_____

My thoughts . . .

_____

_____

_____

_____

_____

_____

_____

_____

229: _____

Tantalizing thought

_____

_____

My thoughts . . .

_____

_____

_____

_____

_____

_____

_____

_____

_____

* 230: _____

_____

_____

_____

* Topic: Isolation

My thoughts . . .

_____

_____

_____

_____

_____

_____

_____

_____

_____

231: _____

Startled lizard stops

_____

_____

My thoughts . . .

_____

_____

_____

_____

_____

_____

_____

_____

_____

232: _____

Finish what you start

_____

_____

My thoughts . . .

_____

_____

_____

_____

_____

_____

_____

_____

_____

233: _____

Zebra disappears

_____

_____

My thoughts . . .

_____

_____

_____

_____

_____

_____

_____

_____

234: _____

I am almost there

_____

_____

My thoughts . . .

_____

_____

_____

_____

_____

_____

_____

_____

235: _____

Sudden precipice

_____

_____

My thoughts . . .

_____

_____

_____

_____

_____

_____

_____

_____

_____

236: _____

Stagnant mossy pond

_____

_____

My thoughts . . .

_____

_____

_____

_____

_____

_____

_____

_____

237: _____

Accept challenges

_____

_____

My thoughts . . .

_____

_____

_____

_____

_____

_____

_____

_____

_____

238: _____

Screeching eagle dives

_____

_____

My thoughts . . .

_____

_____

_____

_____

_____

_____

_____

_____

239: _____

Dance to your own beat

_____

_____

My thoughts . . .

_____

_____

_____

_____

_____

_____

_____

_____

_____

* 240: _____

_____

_____

_____

* Topic: Generosity

My thoughts . . .

_____

_____

_____

_____

_____

_____

_____

_____

_____

_____

241: _____

Heart breaks wide open

_____

_____

My thoughts . . .

_____

_____

_____

_____

_____

_____

_____

_____

_____

242: _____

Best friends forever

_____

_____

My thoughts . . .

_____

_____

_____

_____

_____

_____

_____

_____

_____

243: _____

Ocean mystery

_____

_____

My thoughts . . .

_____

_____

_____

_____

_____

_____

_____

_____

_____

244: _____

Goldfish in a tank

_____

_____

My thoughts . . .

_____

_____

_____

_____

_____

_____

_____

_____

245: _____

Tiny tots toddle

_____

_____

My thoughts . . .

_____

_____

_____

_____

_____

_____

_____

_____

246: _____

Under umbrellas

_____

_____

My thoughts . . .

_____

_____

_____

_____

_____

_____

_____

_____

247: _____

Piping hot coffee

_____

_____

My thoughts . . .

_____

_____

_____

_____

_____

_____

_____

_____

_____

248: _____

Fighting for freedom

_____

_____

My thoughts . . .

_____

_____

_____

_____

_____

_____

_____

_____

249: _____

First passionate kiss

_____

_____

My thoughts . . .

_____

_____

_____

_____

_____

_____

_____

_____

* 250: _____

_____

_____

_____

* Topic: Surprise

My thoughts . . .

_____

_____

_____

_____

_____

_____

_____

_____

_____

251: _____

Backpack filled with food

_____

_____

My thoughts . . .

_____

_____

_____

_____

_____

_____

_____

_____

_____

252: _____

Facing fear alone

_____

_____

My thoughts . . .

_____

_____

_____

_____

_____

_____

_____

_____

_____

253: _____

Dusty furniture

_____

_____

My thoughts . . .

_____

_____

_____

_____

_____

_____

_____

_____

254: _____

First spiky chin hairs

_____

_____

My thoughts . . .

_____

_____

_____

_____

_____

_____

_____

_____

_____

255: _____

Great whale surfaces

_____

_____

My thoughts . . .

_____

_____

_____

_____

_____

_____

_____

_____

_____

256: _____

Ice-coated tree limbs

_____

_____

My thoughts . . .

_____

_____

_____

_____

_____

_____

_____

_____

_____

257: _____

Pulling on blue jeans

_____

_____

My thoughts . . .

_____

_____

_____

_____

_____

_____

_____

_____

_____

258: _____

Just before it blooms

_____

_____

My thoughts . . .

_____

_____

_____

_____

_____

_____

_____

_____

_____

259: _____

Hateful rumors spread

_____

_____

My thoughts . . .

_____

_____

_____

_____

_____

_____

_____

_____

_____

* 260: _____

_____

_____

_____

* Topic: Yellow

My thoughts . . .

_____

_____

_____

_____

_____

_____

_____

_____

_____

261: _____

Surly expression

_____

_____

My thoughts . . .

_____

_____

_____

_____

_____

_____

_____

_____

_____

262: _____

Bugs splat on windshield

_____

_____

My thoughts . . .

_____

_____

_____

_____

_____

_____

_____

_____

263: _____

Children remember

_____

_____

My thoughts . . .

_____

_____

_____

_____

_____

_____

_____

_____

_____

264: _____

Flying high above

_____

_____

My thoughts . . .

_____

_____

_____

_____

_____

_____

_____

_____

265: _____

Black bear leaves her cave

_____

_____

My thoughts . . .

_____

_____

_____

_____

_____

_____

_____

_____

_____

266: _____

Talking to myself

_____

_____

My thoughts . . .

_____

_____

_____

_____

_____

_____

_____

_____

_____

267: _____

Sweat-soaked underarms

_____

_____

My thoughts . . .

_____

_____

_____

_____

_____

_____

_____

_____

268: _____

Fat spider scuttles

_____

_____

My thoughts . . .

_____

_____

_____

_____

_____

_____

_____

_____

269: _____

Insufficient funds

_____

_____

My thoughts . . .

_____

_____

_____

_____

_____

_____

_____

_____

_____

* 270: _____

_____

_____

_____

* Topic: Respect

My thoughts . . .

_____

_____

_____

_____

_____

_____

_____

_____

271: _____

Alligator lurks

_____

_____

My thoughts . . .

_____

_____

_____

_____

_____

_____

_____

_____

272: _____

Choosing how to live

_____

_____

My thoughts . . .

_____

_____

_____

_____

_____

_____

_____

_____

_____

_____

273: _____

Haunting memory

_____

_____

My thoughts . . .

_____

_____

_____

_____

_____

_____

_____

_____

274: _____

Lights turned low tonight

_____

_____

My thoughts . . .

_____

_____

_____

_____

_____

_____

_____

_____

275: _____

Discovering truth

_____

_____

My thoughts . . .

_____

_____

_____

_____

_____

_____

_____

_____

_____

276: _____

Flag flies at half-staff

_____

_____

My thoughts . . .

_____

_____

_____

_____

_____

_____

_____

_____

_____

277: _____

Red carpet treatment

_____

_____

My thoughts . . .

_____

_____

_____

_____

_____

_____

_____

_____

278: _____

Winners ev'ry one

_____

_____

My thoughts . . .

_____

_____

_____

_____

_____

_____

_____

_____

_____

279: _____

No volume control

_____

_____

My thoughts . . .

_____

_____

_____

_____

_____

_____

_____

_____

_____

* 280 : _____

_____

_____

_____

* Topic: Unity

My thoughts . . .

_____

_____

_____

_____

_____

_____

_____

_____

_____

281: _____

Running in circles

_____

_____

My thoughts . . .

_____

_____

_____

_____

_____

_____

_____

_____

_____

282: _____

Friday afternoon

_____

_____

My thoughts . . .

_____

_____

_____

_____

_____

_____

_____

_____

_____

283: _____

Parents' dilemma

_____

_____

My thoughts . . .

_____

_____

_____

_____

_____

_____

_____

_____

_____

284: _____

Little boys will fight

_____

_____

My thoughts . . .

_____

_____

_____

_____

_____

_____

_____

_____

_____

285: _____

Tear rolls down her cheek

_____

_____

My thoughts . . .

_____

_____

_____

_____

_____

_____

_____

_____

_____

286: _____

Change is difficult

_____

_____

My thoughts . . .

_____

_____

_____

_____

_____

_____

_____

_____

287: _____

Suspicions run wild

_____

_____

My thoughts . . .

_____

_____

_____

_____

_____

_____

_____

_____

_____

288: _____

Bizarre disorder

_____

_____

My thoughts . . .

_____

_____

_____

_____

_____

_____

_____

_____

_____

289: _____

Dental procedure

_____

_____

My thoughts . . .

_____

_____

_____

_____

_____

_____

_____

_____

_____

* 290: _____

_____

_____

_____

* Topic: Anticipation

My thoughts . . .

_____

_____

_____

_____

_____

_____

_____

_____

_____

291: _____

Technology-free

_____

_____

My thoughts . . .

_____

_____

_____

_____

_____

_____

_____

_____

_____

292: _____

Biting mosquitos

_____

_____

My thoughts . . .

_____

_____

_____

_____

_____

_____

_____

_____

293: _____

Cracker Jack prizes

_____

_____

My thoughts . . .

_____

_____

_____

_____

_____

_____

_____

_____

_____

294: _____

Tolerant youngster

_____

_____

My thoughts . . .

_____

_____

_____

_____

_____

_____

_____

_____

295: _____

Political zeal

_____

_____

My thoughts . . .

_____

_____

_____

_____

_____

_____

_____

_____

_____

296: _____

Finding shapes in clouds

_____

_____

My thoughts . . .

_____

_____

_____

_____

_____

_____

_____

_____

_____

297: _____

Negotiation

_____

_____

My thoughts . . .

_____

_____

_____

_____

_____

_____

_____

_____

298: _____

Unknown future waits

_____

_____

My thoughts . . .

_____

_____

_____

_____

_____

_____

_____

_____

299: _____

Red streaks across sky

_____

_____

My thoughts . . .

_____

_____

_____

_____

_____

_____

_____

_____

_____

* 300: _____

_____

_____

_____

* Topic: Spring

My thoughts . . .

_____

_____

_____

_____

_____

_____

_____

_____

_____

301: _____

Fish bite at daybreak

_____

_____

My thoughts . . .

_____

_____

_____

_____

_____

_____

_____

_____

_____

302: _____

Missing lost loved ones

_____

_____

My thoughts . . .

_____

_____

_____

_____

_____

_____

_____

_____

_____

303: _____

Exquisite beauty

_____

_____

My thoughts . . .

_____

_____

_____

_____

_____

_____

_____

_____

_____

304: _____

Surprisingly strong

_____

_____

My thoughts . . .

_____

_____

_____

_____

_____

_____

_____

_____

_____

305: _____

Violent earthquake

_____

_____

My thoughts . . .

_____

_____

_____

_____

_____

_____

_____

_____

_____

306: _____

Man sits next to me

_____

_____

My thoughts . . .

_____

_____

_____

_____

_____

_____

_____

_____

_____

307: _____

Raindrops on puddles

_____

_____

My thoughts . . .

_____

_____

_____

_____

_____

_____

_____

_____

_____

308: _____

Sweet summer corn cobs

_____

_____

My thoughts . . .

_____

_____

_____

_____

_____

_____

_____

_____

309: _____

No dessert tonight

_____

_____

My thoughts . . .

_____

_____

_____

_____

_____

_____

_____

_____

* 310: _____

_____

_____

_____

* Topic: Rain

My thoughts . . .

_____

_____

_____

_____

_____

_____

_____

_____

_____

311: _____

Freckle-faced ginger

_____

_____

My thoughts . . .

_____

_____

_____

_____

_____

_____

_____

_____

312: _____

Self-satisfaction

_____

_____

My thoughts . . .

_____

_____

_____

_____

_____

_____

_____

_____

_____

_____

313: _____

Chocolate river

_____

_____

My thoughts . . .

_____

_____

_____

_____

_____

_____

_____

_____

_____

314: _____

Cultural exchange

_____

_____

My thoughts . . .

_____

_____

_____

_____

_____

_____

_____

_____

_____

315: _____

Never can go back

_____

_____

My thoughts . . .

_____

_____

_____

_____

_____

_____

_____

_____

_____

316: _____

Flood water recedes

_____

_____

My thoughts . . .

_____

_____

_____

_____

_____

_____

_____

_____

317: _____

Out-grown swing set rusts

_____

_____

My thoughts . . .

_____

_____

_____

_____

_____

_____

_____

_____

318: _____

Tooth under pillow

_____

_____

My thoughts . . .

_____

_____

_____

_____

_____

_____

_____

_____

_____

319: _____

Trying to ignore

_____

_____

My thoughts . . .

_____

_____

_____

_____

_____

_____

_____

_____

_____

* 320: _____

_____

_____

_____

* Topic: White

My thoughts . . .

_____

_____

_____

_____

_____

_____

_____

_____

_____

321: _____

Underwear wedgie

_____

_____

My thoughts . . .

_____

_____

_____

_____

_____

_____

_____

_____

_____

322: _____

Listen to silence

_____

_____

My thoughts . . .

_____

_____

_____

_____

_____

_____

_____

_____

323: _____

Not ready to die

_____

_____

My thoughts . . .

_____

_____

_____

_____

_____

_____

_____

_____

324: _____

Tattoo artist weeps

_____

_____

My thoughts . . .

_____

_____

_____

_____

_____

_____

_____

_____

325: _____

Lights in the distance

_____

_____

My thoughts . . .

_____

_____

_____

_____

_____

_____

_____

_____

_____

326: _____

Computer children

_____

_____

My thoughts . . .

_____

_____

_____

_____

_____

_____

_____

_____

327: _____

Sibling rivalry

_____

_____

My thoughts . . .

_____

_____

_____

_____

_____

_____

_____

_____

_____

328: _____

Flowers bloom at last

_____

_____

My thoughts . . .

_____

_____

_____

_____

_____

_____

_____

_____

329: _____

Insincere laughter

_____

_____

My thoughts . . .

_____

_____

_____

_____

_____

_____

_____

_____

_____

* 330: _____

_____

_____

_____

* Topic: Growth

My thoughts . . .

_____

_____

_____

_____

_____

_____

_____

_____

331: _____

Blue jeans way too tight

_____

_____

My thoughts . . .

_____

_____

_____

_____

_____

_____

_____

_____

_____

332: _____

Friends are like cupcakes

_____

_____

My thoughts . . .

_____

_____

_____

_____

_____

_____

_____

_____

_____

333: _____

Mountain lion slinks

_____

_____

My thoughts . . .

_____

_____

_____

_____

_____

_____

_____

_____

_____

334: _____

One's identity

_____
_____

My thoughts . . .

_____
_____
_____
_____
_____
_____
_____
_____
_____

335: _____

Mother screams, child breathes

_____

_____

My thoughts . . .

_____

_____

_____

_____

_____

_____

_____

_____

_____

336: _____

First day at new school

_____

_____

My thoughts . . .

_____

_____

_____

_____

_____

_____

_____

_____

_____

337: _____

What I cannot keep

_____

_____

My thoughts . . .

_____

_____

_____

_____

_____

_____

_____

_____

_____

338: _____

Diamond ring sparkles

_____

_____

My thoughts . . .

_____

_____

_____

_____

_____

_____

_____

_____

_____

339: _____

Pouring out my soul

_____

_____

My thoughts . . .

_____

_____

_____

_____

_____

_____

_____

_____

* 340: _____

_____

_____

_____

* Topic: Appreciation

My thoughts . . .

_____

_____

_____

_____

_____

_____

_____

_____

341: _____

Keep your eyes open

_____

_____

My thoughts . . .

_____

_____

_____

_____

_____

_____

_____

_____

342: _____

Perilous riptide

_____

_____

My thoughts . . .

_____

_____

_____

_____

_____

_____

_____

_____

343: _____

Ice crystals coat glass

_____

_____

My thoughts . . .

_____

_____

_____

_____

_____

_____

_____

_____

344: _____

Fire consumes forest

_____

_____

My thoughts . . .

_____

_____

_____

_____

_____

_____

_____

_____

_____

345: _____

Spider web glistens

_____

_____

My thoughts . . .

_____

_____

_____

_____

_____

_____

_____

_____

_____

346: _____

Pandora's gift box

_____

_____

My thoughts . . .

_____

_____

_____

_____

_____

_____

_____

_____

347: _____

Cleaning my junk drawer

_____

_____

My thoughts . . .

_____

_____

_____

_____

_____

_____

_____

_____

348: _____

Today, tomorrow

_____

_____

My thoughts . . .

_____

_____

_____

_____

_____

_____

_____

_____

_____

_____

349: _____

Non-GMO food

_____

_____

My thoughts . . .

_____

_____

_____

_____

_____

_____

_____

_____

_____

* 350: _____

_____

_____

_____

* Topic: Love

My thoughts . . .

_____

_____

_____

_____

_____

_____

_____

_____

_____

351: _____

Growing like a weed

_____

_____

My thoughts . . .

_____

_____

_____

_____

_____

_____

_____

_____

_____

352: _____

Natural talent

_____

_____

My thoughts . . .

_____

_____

_____

_____

_____

_____

_____

_____

_____

353: _____

Double rainbow glows

_____

_____

My thoughts . . .

_____

_____

_____

_____

_____

_____

_____

_____

_____

354: _____

Discrimination

_____

_____

My thoughts . . .

_____

_____

_____

_____

_____

_____

_____

_____

355: _____

Elephant lumbers

_____

_____

My thoughts . . .

_____

_____

_____

_____

_____

_____

_____

_____

_____

356: _____

Lemon squirts my eye

_____

_____

My thoughts . . .

_____

_____

_____

_____

_____

_____

_____

_____

_____

357: _____

Gale winds whip treetops

_____

_____

My thoughts . . .

_____

_____

_____

_____

_____

_____

_____

_____

_____

358: _____

Mona Lisa smiles

_____

_____

My thoughts . . .

_____

_____

_____

_____

_____

_____

_____

_____

359: _____

Youthful plan unfolds

_____

_____

My thoughts . . .

_____

_____

_____

_____

_____

_____

_____

_____

_____

* 360: _____

_____

_____

_____

* Topic: Success

My thoughts . . .

_____

_____

_____

_____

_____

_____

_____

_____

_____

361: _____

Worst nightmare ever

_____

_____

My thoughts . . .

_____

_____

_____

_____

_____

_____

_____

_____

362: _____

Believe in something

_____

_____

My thoughts . . .

_____

_____

_____

_____

_____

_____

_____

_____

_____

363: _____

Morning's new message

_____

_____

My thoughts . . .

_____

_____

_____

_____

_____

_____

_____

_____

364: _____

Hummingbird vigor

_____

_____

My thoughts . . .

_____

_____

_____

_____

_____

_____

_____

_____

365: _____

Ev'ry day's special

_____

_____

My thoughts . . .

_____

_____

_____

_____

_____

_____

_____

_____

_____

366: _____

In my next lifetime

_____

_____

My thoughts . . .

_____

_____

_____

_____

_____

_____

_____

_____

GUEST

HAIKU

CONTRIBUTORS

with their notes of inspiration

Allow the following poems to guide and inspire!

I would like to acknowledge each of these contributors along with my friends and family for encouraging me to create this haiku starter journal.

Extra-special thanks to my husband, Mike, who continues to support me in every way.

> My love for you grows
> With each passing year, you are
> my inspiration

I do hope you enjoy this book!

If you do:

> Share one with a friend
> See if they can haiku too
> Prepare for surprise

Guest Haiku Contributions

The best gifts come in
No packages at all but
In the heart of friends

Happiness is a
Quality of heart that leads
To fun and laughter

Attitude is life…
Saving esprit like fresh air
Keep it positive

~ Janet Sheppard Kelleher, author of ***Big C, little ta-ta***

Janet's inspiration comes from her battle with—and victory over—breast cancer since the year 2000.

~ ~ ~

Eyes closed, heart open
Longing for enlightenment
Basking in stillness

~ Nadine Collier, Professional Counselor/Life Coach

"My inspiration was my experience witnessing a sunset over Lake Michigan. I have been trying to practice mindfulness."

Hide and seek at dusk
Honey bee, dime store, drive-in
Land line, living wage

~ Judy W. Cole, Poet

"It was one of those drowsy moments before full consciousness during which I often haunt the places of my younger days, and I found myself mentally wandering around in some of the stores I frequented as a child, one of them being a dime store. Surfacing closer to consciousness, I asked myself if 5 and dimes even exist anymore. And drive-in movies? I started listing things gone by . . ."

~ ~ ~

Pilot's announcement:
"Leaving Vietnam airspace"
Cheers, laughter, relief

~ John O. Stewart, CW3, US Army (Ret)

"This was part of a series of haikus about my experiences in Vietnam. It pertains to the flight out of country back to America at the end of my tour with a planeload of other soldiers and military personnel."

Every child has
a tone of voice, an eye roll
to make her mom nuts

"Did you say 'haiku'?"
"I did! I did say 'haiku'!"
"Well, then - gesundheit!"

Sarcasm is a
language skill that is sadly
lost on dogs and cats

~ Maggie Lamond Simone, national award-winning
columnist and author of *Body Punishment* and *From
Beer to Maternity*

Maggie's last poem "is inspired by my daily
interaction with my pets - my dog, as he sniffs every
single blade of grass on our walk to see what might
have changed from the day before, and my cats, who
actually wait for me to clean their litter boxes before
they will use them in the morning."

~ ~ ~

"I've been out of it
for half of my life," she says
at the kitchen sink

~ Carol Bellhouse, attorney and author of 19 books
and 23 scripts

The inspiration for Carol's poem comes from "words
actually spoken by my mother recently."

Pretty party dress
on bus; boy's awkward comment
Now two red faces

Old men playing cards
Blossoms, bus fumes, honking horns,
Springtime in the Bronx

~ John Paul McKinney, author of ***Charlie's Angle***

John Paul's first poem was ". . . inspired by an incident on the New York City subway. Two young ladies (probably 12 or 13) got on, clearly ready for a party, each carrying a present and dressed in pretty dresses. The rather rough looking adolescent sitting next to me blurted out to one of them, "You're really purdy." She blushed and put her head down until their stop and then rushed off as the young man yelled apologetically, "I didn't mean anything wrong. I just think you are."

His second poem was ". . . based on my time in New York as a graduate student. One of my fondest memories is of going for walks along Fordham Road, especially in the spring. These are the images I remember."

Bent-backed grandmothers
Harajuki Lolitas
Dancing, old and new

Black-clad students stream
Chattering, station to school
New school year begins

Salaryman weeps
Empty subway car rattles
Midnight melody

~ Stephanie R. Sorensen, author of *Tôru: Wayfarer Returns*

"My experience of Japan was urban, school and work and entertainment, not nature and silence. I don't hear Basho's frog jumping into a still pool. Instead I experience the omnipresent subway trains, the roar of traffic. Seasons are marked by cherry blossoms, but also by black-uniformed students flowing like a river when school resumes in the fall. Isolation in an urban setting by a lonely drunk salaryman coming home late. The passage of time by the huge generation gap between the young dancing girls and their boom boxes in Harajuku and the elderly grandmothers, in worn kimono, inching their way home from the store."

[a special thanks to Stephanie for her suggestion to scatter an occasional topic throughout the book!]

Softly the rain falls,
Come, sit with me for a while
Before flakes descend.

The gypsy is sad,
Tambourine wails his sad cry -
To have loved again.

~ Susan Matthews, HEA

Susan's describes her poetic inspiration in the form of haiku. For her first poem, "Live in a small town / Where making true friends is hard / In changing weather."

For her second, "I always wonder / About how a gypsy sings / When his loss is great."

~ ~ ~

Rocks and hard places
between the lines on a page,
Scribble where you can

~ Andrew Wallace, Poet

"Sometimes a writer's creative life is blocked by uncontrollable circumstances, and the only option is to forge ahead. The poem is no way an endorsement of graffiti."

Glorious colors
Seeping from heaven's pallet
Melting our troubles

Gathering fun day
Clothing, bags, gowns, and jewels
On to the wedding

Solitude, strange, deep
Stirs me on to quiet thought
Just one place setting

~ Patricia Bernier, artist, poet, Laurel's Mum

Inspiration for Patricia's first poem: "Looking out my window over the ocean and sky always puts me in awe of creation."

Her second poem was inspired by "impressions on the day of Pat and Alex's wedding," and her third poem was written "a short while after my husband's death."

~ ~ ~

White sky hovers long
Ice peaks on mountains rolling
Birds' song opens doors

~ Jennifer Sweete, Author, Dragon Hunter, Cat Enthusiast

"Inspired by my back yard, Springtime 2016, Allelujia!"

"Write what you know." No.
Not for me. The muse demands:
Seek out the unknown.

~ Ann Parker, author of the award-winning *Silver Rush Mystery* series

"My entire writing career has evolved from 'writing what I *don't* know'—approaching each new, unfamiliar subject with curiosity, enthusiasm, and a deep appreciation of serendipity. The drive to learn and to share what I discover has powered me through the decades. In writing fiction, which I came to relatively late in life, it has been no different."

~ ~ ~

Crash flash fire death help
Horrible scenario
To serve we practice

All in place action
Do this do that get it right
Vigilant practice

~ Nancy Schloerke, Director, Lake County Public Library

Nancy's poems "are inspired by my participation as a volunteer for the Public Information Office during a major annual emergency training exercise."

In doing this task
I have sadly discovered
I suck at haiku

Authentic pain is
found turning from true purpose
to fear's illusions

Think I'm finished now
Grey matter cannot corral
Wildly wired words

~ Stefanie Foreman, "Being"

Stefanie's second poem is inspired by ". . . how many of us are stuck in our so-called 'comfort zone.' How so many people won't take the risk to go for what they really want to do because of the fear-based stories we tell ourselves."

~ ~ ~

Winds aloft twist, dance
Magician-like, fingers form
Clear air into cloud

~ Maria Weber, author of *I'll Be There to Write the Story: A Mother-Daughter Journey Beyond Death*

Maria reminds us that the "haiku should stand alone without the photo to be a good haiku allowing the mind's eye of the reader to create the picture."

About the Author:

Laurel McHargue likes
inspiring emotional
response in others

She's hooked on haiku
Wondering if you are now
hooked on haiku too!

**Follow Laurel on her blog and sign up for her
mid-monthly newsletter at
www.leadvillelaurel.com
"Like" her on Facebook at
https://www.facebook.com/LeadvilleLaurel/
and feel free to email her at
laurel.mchargue@gmail.com**

**Find other books by Laurel on Amazon
or request them from your local book store!**

Take this journal with you when you know you'll be spending time in waiting rooms, long lines, airplanes, bathrooms . . .